Kamala's Art

by Yuri Lubov
illustrated by Mary Young

HOUGHTON MIFFLIN HARCOURT
School Publishers

Printed in China

ISBN-13: 978-0-547-42743-0
ISBN-10: 0-547-42743-3

5 6 7 8 0940 18 17 16 15 14 13 12
4500345273

This is Kamala.
She lives in a zoo
with many other animals.
A lion, a tiger, and
a bear live there, too.

Kamala is not like
the other animals.
She can paint pictures!
Many people are head over
heels about her paintings.

Kamala did not have
a teacher.
One day a zoo worker
gave Kamala some paper
and some paint.

Kamala picked up a
brush with her trunk.
She dipped the brush in
paint and pushed it
along the paper.

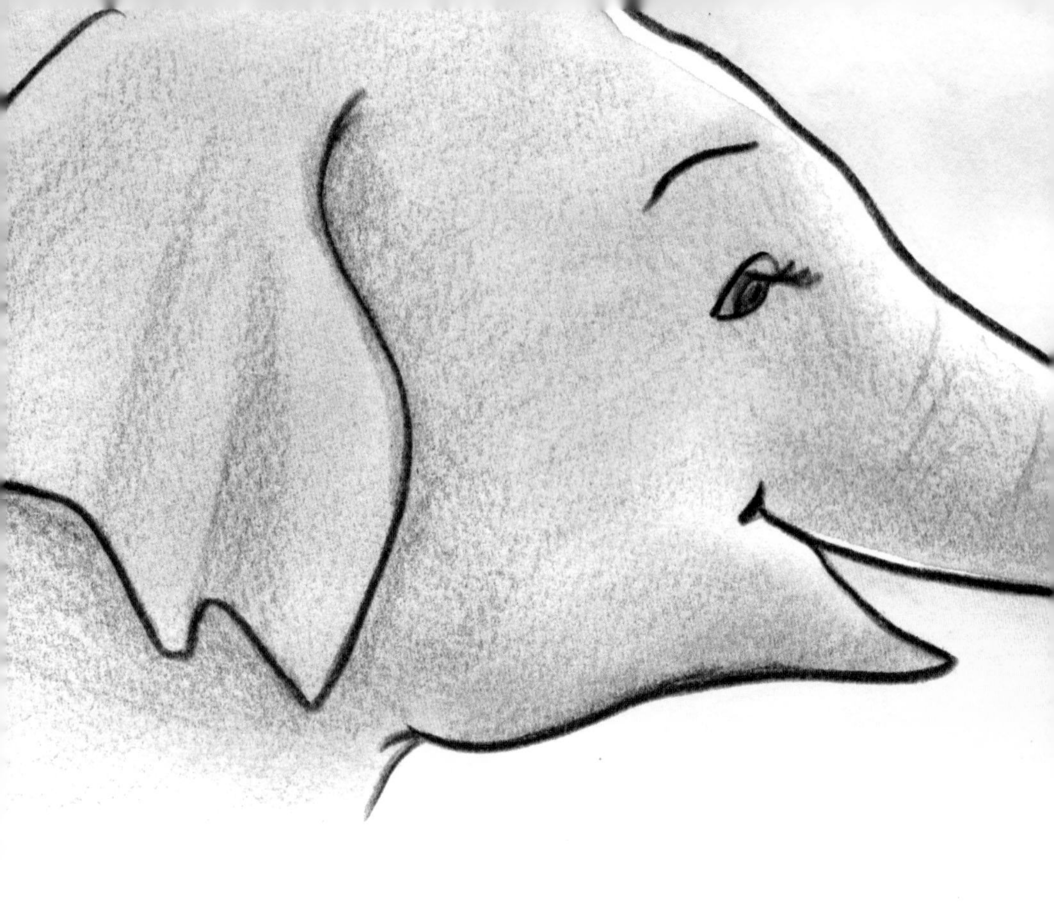

At first Kamala surprised
everyone at the zoo.
She liked to paint!
Now, she even mixes
colors when she paints.

Kamala makes a line
with yellow paint toward
the side of the paper.
Then she draws a red line.
Kamala makes... orange!

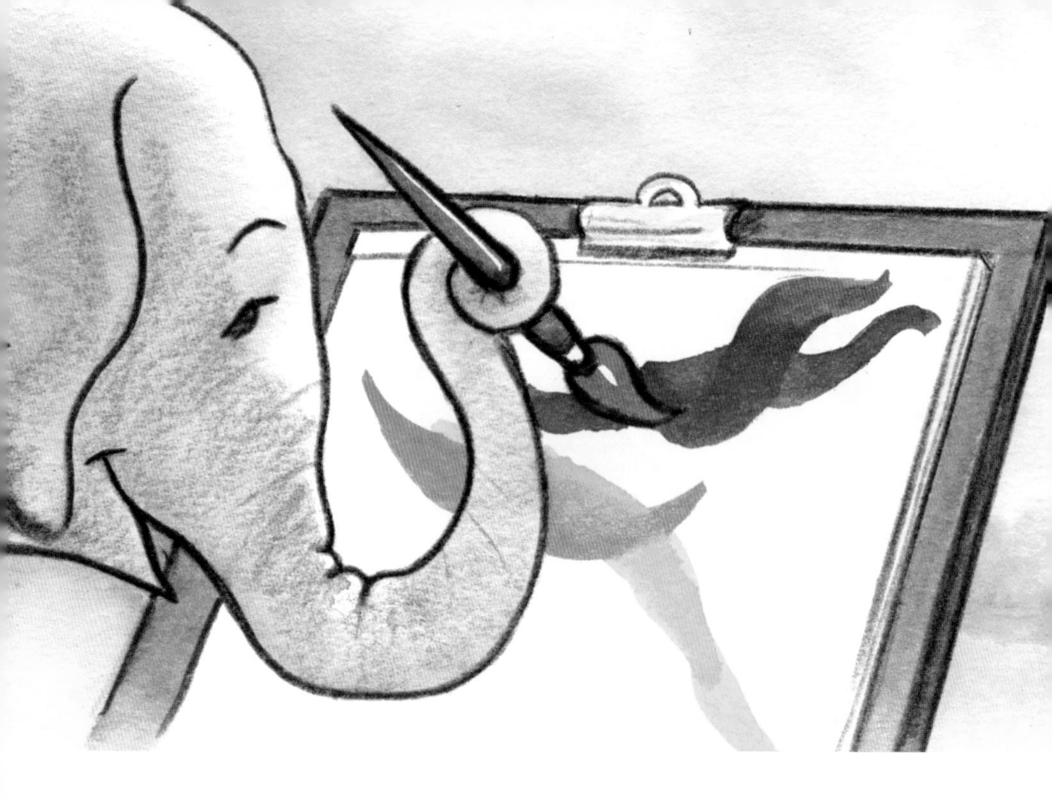

Kamala makes a blue line
above the orange one.
Then she dips her brush
in the red paint.
She makes... purple!

Many people have studied
Kamala's paintings.
Some think her pictures
are just marks on a page.
Some people think the
pictures are great art.

Many people keep
an eye on Kamala.
They can't wait to see
what she will paint next!

Responding

WORDS TO KNOW Word Builder

What words tell about a bear?

Write About It

Text to World Kamala likes to draw. You can draw too. Draw a picture of a bear. Show where the bear lives. Write a sentence about your picture.

WORDS TO KNOW

above	**studied**
bear	**surprised**
even	**teacher**
pushed	**toward**

TARGET STRATEGY Monitor/Clarify

Find ways to figure out what doesn't make sense.